MY LITTLE BROTHER'S A
ZOMBIE

Franklin Watts
First published in Great Britain in 2018 by The Watts Publishing Group

Text copyright © Tony Lee 2018
Illustration copyright © Pedro J. Columbo 2018

Illustrator: Pedro J. Columbo
Design Manager: Peter Scoulding
Cover Designer: Cathryn Gilbert
Production Manager: Robert Dale
Series Consultant: Paul Register
Executive Editor: Adrian Cole

HB ISBN 978 1 4451 5708 5
PB ISBN 978 1 4451 5709 2
Library ebook ISBN 978 1 4451 5710 8

Printed in China

Franklin Watts
An imprint of
Hachette Children's Group
Part of The Watts Publishing Group
Carmelite House
50 Victoria Embankment
London EC4Y 0DZ

An Hachette UK Company
www.hachette.co.uk

www.franklinwatts.co.uk

MY LITTLE BROTHER'S A
ZOMBIE

TONY LEE AND PEDRO J. COLUMBO

LONDON·SYDNEY

SCRITCH!
SCRATCH!
SCRITCH!

SCRATCH!

PETEY!
I KNOW
THAT'S YOU.
STOP IT.

WURRRGH....

I'M
SERIOUS!
STOP OR
I'M TELLING
MUM!

CREAK

SLAM!

WURRRGH!!!!

BRAIINNNSSS!!!

BRAINS.

MUM! HE'S DOING IT AGAIN!

I'M TRYING TO DO MY HOMEWORK!

LEWIS - HE'S SIX. IT'S JUST A PHASE, HE'LL GROW OUT OF IT.

IN THE MEANTIME, LOCK THE DOOR.

MEET MY BROTHER, PETEY.

PETEY LOVES **ZOMBIES**. AND I MEAN **LOVES** THEM.

HE'S GOT COMICS, BOOKS, GAMES – **EVERYTHING** HE DOES IS ZOMBIE RELATED.

HIS ROOM IS **FILLED** WITH ZOMBIES – POSTERS, DUVET COVERS – EVEN A **ZOMBIE NIGHT LIGHT**.

PETEY'S **FRIENDS** DON'T LIKE PLAYING ZOMBIES ...

... BUT THAT'S OKAY AS ZOMBIE **NEED** SOMEONE TO CHASE.

GRAARH!

PETEY!

HE EVEN **EATS** LIKE A ZOMBIE.

IT'S DRIVING ME MAD!

SHOW HIM A **REAL** ZOMBIE FILM. ONE OF THE 'LIVING DEAD' ONES. THAT'LL STOP HIM.

HE'S SIX YEARS OLD, MOLLY. ONE OF THOSE WOULD **TRAUMATISE** HIM!

AND HOW HAVE **YOU** SEEN IT ANYWAY? YOU'RE **ELEVEN!**

THIS IS MY BEST FRIEND MOLLY. SHE WANTS TO BE A **MOVIE DIRECTOR** WHEN SHE GROWS UP.

I'VE SEEN THINGS. MY **BIG BROTHER** SHOWED ME.

THE DIRECTING'S **TERRIBLE**, THOUGH. AND THE SCRIPT'S SO **CHEESY.**

I'M HAPPY TO JUST BE **WITH HER** WHEN I GROW UP.

BUT IF YOU TELL **ANYONE** I SAID THAT I'LL **DENY** IT, OKAY?

TODAY WE SHALL BE REANIMATING THESE **DEAD FROGS** WITH ELECTRICITY!

I **HATE** BIOLOGY.

IT'S ALL RIGH WHEN **MISTE FLAPPERS** ISN'T DOING I

NOW! **ATTACH THE ELECTRIC PRONGS!**

BRING THESE BEAUTIES **TO LIFE!**

URGH - IT **TWITCHED!**

SPLOOSH!

THANKS MRS CHANG! SEE YOU NEXT WEEK!

GLUB.

WHAT DID YOU DO?

IT WASN'T MY FAULT. A JAR OF **GOOP** JUMPED OUT AT ME.

LET'S GET OUT OF HERE BEFORE I HAVE TO **PAY** FOR WHATEVER EXPENSIVE THING YOU JUST BROKE!

- YAWN -

BRAINS.

PETEY, WHAT ARE YOU DOING IN MY **ROOM?** GO BACK TO BED --

BRAINS.

AAAAAIIIEEEEE

OUTSIDE SCHOOL.

I GOT YOUR TEXT - WHAT'S THE PROBLEM?

THIS IS. I THINK SOMETHING **MAGICAL** HIT HIM WHILE WE WERE IN MRS CHANG'S SHOP.

OH. OH **WOW.**

WE NEED TO SEE MISTER FLAPPERS!

LEWIS! IT'S SATURDAY! NO SCHOOL ON SATURDAYS!

JUST ME AND MY... **EXPERIMENTS!**

YOU KNOW YOU SAID IF I EVER FOUND A **ZOMBIE** I SHOULD BRING HIM TO YOU?

WELL... I FOUND A **ZOMBIE.**

BRAINS.

LEWIS, YOU CAN'T KEEP HIM IN **HERE!**

WELL I'M NOT LETTING OLD **FLAPPERS** GET HIS HANDS ON HIM EITHER!

WHAT **OTHER** OPTION DO WE HAVE?

GO BACK TO MRS CHA EXPLAIN WH HAPPENED. MIGHT HAVE CURE!

I'LL MAKE SURE PETEY STAYS PUT - AND STOP **YOUR MUM** FROM SEEING HIM!

BUT I'M ONLY DOING THIS BECAUSE I **LIKE** YOU.

SHE **LIKES** ME!

MISTER FLAPPERS HAS PETEY! HE'S GOING TO **EXPERIMENT** ON HIM!

MISTER FLAPPERS IS **LOVELY**! CAN'T BELIE HE'D DO THA

MURGH?

YOU STAY COMFORTABLE, LITTLE ZOMBIE!

THESE ARE FOR YOUR OWN SAFTEY - FOR WHEN THE... **CONVULSING**... STARTS!

WHEN I SAY GO -- YOU HIT THAT **TRIANGLE** WITH ALL YOUR MIGHT.

OHO! THIS'LL GIVE YOU A LITTLE SHOCK!

JUST LIKE A **POOR LITTLE FROGGIE**!

POLICE! BACK AWAY FROM THE BOY!

CRASHH!

HE'S NOT A BOY! HE'S A ZOMBIE!

HE'S DEAD! HONEST!

HE DOESN'T LOOK DEAD TO ME! HE LOOKS TERRIFIED!

ASK THE GIRL! SHE KNOWS WHAT I MEAN!

I HAVE NO IDEA WHAT HE'S TALKING ABOUT.

HE'S INHALED TOO MUCH SCIENCE GAS - AND IT'S AFFECTED HIS BRAIN!

THANKS, MOLLY. I'M GLAD LEWIS HAS YOU FOR A GIRLFRIEND.

WE'RE JUST FRIENDS.

OF COURSE YOU ARE.

IT WORKED! THEY'RE BACK TO NORMAL!

OF COURSE THEY ARE! AND YOUR BROTHER WILL BE TOO!

BUT WE DO NEED TO TALK ABOUT HOW THIS STARTED. YOUR BROTHER BROKE A **VERY EXPENSIVE BOTTLE**.

IT'S **MY** FAULT, I SHOULD HAVE WATCHED HIM BETTER.

I CAN WORK TO PAY FOR THE DAMAGE.

WELL, MY SON IS AWAY, SO I COULD USE A **SATURDAY ASSISTANT** FOR A MONTH.

I COULD ALSO TEACH YOU **MAGIC**. YOUR **SKILLS** WERE EVIDENT IN THE RITUAL.

REALLY? I WAS THAT GOOD?

OF COURSE NOT!

I DID ALL THE WORK - ALL YOU DID WAS **HIT A TRIANGLE**!

NOW **GO** FIND YOUR BROTHER!

THANK YOU MRS CHANG!

YOU KNOW, I'M SURE THERE'S **SOMETHING MORE** GOING ON HERE.

I DON'T KNOW WHAT YOU MEAN!

I MEAN, I HAVEN'T SEEN **THAT MUCH MAGIC** FLYING AROUND -

- SINCE I **WORKED SATURDAYS** FOR **MRS CHANG.**

WHAT ABOUT MISTER FLAPPERS?

OH, IT SEEMS THERE WAS A **GAS LEAK** IN THE CLASSROOM, AND HE INHALED IT.

MADE HIM THINK PETEY WAS A **ZOMBIE.** HE'LL BE ALL RIGHT IN A WEEK OR TWO.

I DON'T THINK I **LIKE** ZOMBIE STORIES ANYMORE.

HAHAHAHA!

THE END...?